KT-393-590

Key Stage 2
Grammar

Carol Matchett

Name _____

Schofield & Sims

Introduction

Grammar is all about using words effectively. It is not just about grammatical rules – it's about getting your message across so that everyone understands you. It's about making your writing sound effective, so that everyone wants to read it.

This book will help you understand different aspects of grammar. As your understanding improves, so will your writing. The book begins by describing the different types of words and why they are important. It then goes on to explain how these words can be put together in sentences.

Finding your way around this book

Before you start using this book, write your name in the name box on the first page.

Then decide how to begin. If you want a complete course on grammar, you should work right through the book from beginning to end. Another way to use the book is to dip into it when you want to find out about a particular topic. The contents page will help you to find the pages you need. Whichever way you choose, don't try to do too much at once – it's better to work through the book in short bursts.

When you have found the topic you want to study, look out for these icons, which mark different parts of the text. Right at the end of the book (page 64) you will find a useful grammar checklist to use when you are writing.

Activities

This icon shows you the activities that you should complete. You write your answers in the spaces provided. After you have worked through all the activities on the page, turn to pages 49 to 63 to check your answers. When you are sure that you understand the topic, put a tick in the box beside it on the Contents page. **Revision of word classes** on page 21 will remind you of the topics that you have worked through so far. The **Editing and Revising** activities on pages 22, 24, 31 and 39 will check your understanding. On pages 25 and 48 you will find suggestions for some projects (**Now you try!**), which will give you further practice in grammar.

 ### Explanation

This text explains the topic and gives examples. Read it before you start the activities.

 ### Notes

Some extra things that you need to know about the topic.

 ### Information

This text gives you useful background information about the subject. Surprise your friends with some fascinating facts!

Contents

Tick the box when you have worked through the topic.

Nouns

Nouns are words that **name** things. **Common nouns** are the words that we use every day to talk about objects, animals, places and people. They name different kinds of things.

For example: table   pencil   dog   rabbit   school   park   girl   man

Proper nouns are the special names we give to a **particular** person, animal or place.

For example: Rachel   Lee   Tiddles   Champion   Manchester

1. Write a **common noun** in each box to complete these sentences. Your sentences can be sensible or funny. The first sentence has been completed for you, in two different ways.

a) The ⬚cat⬚ sat on the ⬚wall⬚ . Or The ⬚elephant⬚ sat on the ⬚hat⬚ .

b) A ⬚⬚ jumped over the ⬚⬚ .

c) My ⬚⬚ threw the ⬚⬚ into the ⬚⬚ .

d) The ⬚⬚ was waiting for a ⬚⬚ .

e) Asleep on the ⬚⬚ there was a great big ⬚⬚ .

2. Think of a **proper noun** (a special name) for each of these **common nouns**. Remember to use a capital letter at the start of the name.

a) _Cuddles_   the cat

b) _____   the fish

c) _____   the hamster

d) _____   the dog

e) _____   the snake

f) _____   the lizard

Did you know...

The idea of proper nouns, or special names, was invented hundreds of years ago when people realised that sometimes an ordinary common noun was not enough. For example, as long as there was only one town in the area, then the word *town* was fine – everyone knew which place it referred to. But as soon as there was more than one town nearby, people needed a way of knowing which town was which. So each town was given its own special name and place names were invented.

Nouns

When you are writing, common nouns are sometimes not very useful. Some common nouns cover lots of different sorts of things.

For example, if you use the words a man

he might be...   a farmer...   a policeman...   a pop star.

When you are writing, you need to be precise. Choose nouns carefully. Some nouns don't give the reader a clear picture.

For example: The **man** ran out of the **building**.

What sort of man was he? What was the building like?

The reader gets a much clearer picture if you write:

The **fire-fighter** ran out of the **tower block**.

or   The **robber** ran out of the **bank**.

3. Add some more **precise** nouns that you could use in place of these everyday nouns.

Cake	**Dog**	**Building**
chocolate éclair	husky	supermarket

4. Change the common nouns in these sentences for more interesting choices.

elephant   bananas

a) The ~~animal~~ stole the ~~fruit~~.

b) The ~~dog~~ ran into the ~~shop~~.

c) The ~~lady~~ stood in the middle of the ~~room~~.

d) The ~~man~~ put on his ~~clothes~~.

e) The ~~group of people~~ came out of the ~~building~~.

Adjectives

Adjectives are **describing words**. They tell you more about a noun. Adjectives help to give the reader a clearer picture of what is being described.

For example: The walker was **exhausted** as he climbed the **steep** hill.

The adjectives in this sentence help us to picture the walker and the hill.

1. Read this description. Underline the **adjectives** that help you to picture the scene. In the box, draw the scene exactly as it is described.

The winding path led her as far as the crumbling walls of an abandoned building. The walls were overgrown with ivy and the floor was scattered with rough bricks and rubble.

2. Make an 'abc' of adjectives! Write an **adjective** next to each letter of the alphabet shown below. For each letter, choose an **adjective** that describes the animals. Make sure the words you choose are adjectives.

a	_angry_	alligators	n		nightingales
b	_brown_	bears	o		otters
c		crocodiles	p		pandas
d		ducks	q		quails
e		elephants	r		rats
f		foxes	s		snakes
g		gorillas	t		tigers
h		hippos	u		umbrella birds
i		insects	v		vultures
j		jackals	w		whales
k		kangaroos	x		x
l		lions	y		yaks
m		monkeys	z	_zany_	zebras

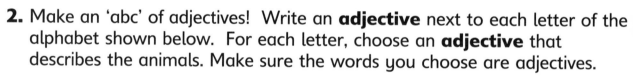

I can't think of an animal or an adjective beginning with 'x' – can you?!

Adjectives

Adjectives help to make your writing more **interesting**. As with nouns, choose adjectives carefully to make sure that you give your reader a clear picture of what you are describing.

3. Adjectives can give you extra information about size, colour, qualities (that means what things are like) or moods. Write some more **adjectives** in these boxes.

Size	Colour	Qualities	Moods
enormous	golden	ugly	angry

4. Write an **adjective** in each box to complete this description.

The sky was _____ and _____ . It was _____ and

a few _____ flakes of snow were beginning to fall. Suddenly out

of the gloom a _____ figure appeared hurrying down the road.

The figure was _____ and _____ .

It was wearing a _____ _____ cloak.

5. In the box, draw a picture of a castle. Write down some adjectives to describe different aspects of this setting.

a) _____ walls

b) _____ windows

c) _____ door

d) _____ turrets

e) _____ flags

Comparatives and superlatives

Sometimes, adjectives are used to compare two things. Adjectives like this are called **comparative adjectives**.

For example: Mrs Jones is **old**. *an adjective*

Mrs Jones is **older than** Mr Jackson.

▲

a comparative adjective

Sometimes, adjectives are used to show the most or the least of everything. Adjectives like this are called **superlatives**.

For example: Mrs Jones is the **oldest** person on our street.

1. Complete this chart of **comparative** and **superlative adjectives**.

a) clever ▶ *cleverer* ▶ *cleverest*

b) strong ▶ _____ ▶ _____

c) fast ▶ _____ ▶ _____

d) cold ▶ _____ ▶ _____

> **notes**
> Sometimes we make **comparatives** by using the words **more** or **less** (for example: *more beautiful, less intelligent*). Sometimes we make **superlatives** by using the words **most** or **least** (for example: *most anxious, least surprising*).

2. Complete these boastful sentences by adding a **comparative adjective** and a suitable ending.

a) My dad is ___*cleverer*___ than ___*the winner of Mastermind.*___

b) Our dog is _____ than _____

c) My sister is _____ than _____

d) Our car is _____ than _____

3. Choose the best **superlative** from the box to complete these adverts.

a) Wheat-a-Flakes – the _____ cereal yet.

b) Don't miss the _____ film of the year.

c) Test-drive the _____ car on the track.

d) This is the _____ ice cream ever tasted.

> **fastest**
> **funniest**
> **crunchiest**
> **creamiest**

Plurals

Plural means **more than one** of something. Quite often we make plurals just by **adding an 's'** to the end of the noun.

For example: a dog ▶ lots of dogs   a car ▶ lots of cars

Sometimes, there is a different word when we talk about more than one of something.

For example: a child ▶ lots of children   a mouse ▶ lots of mice

1. Here is a shopping list for a birthday party. You will need **more than one** of everything on the list. Turn the items on the list into **plurals**.

   a) |12| packets of crisps

   b) ☐ pizza

   c) ☐ cake

   d) ☐ cookie

   e) ☐ bottle of pop

   f) ☐ bag of balloon

   g) ☐ pack of streamer

> **Did you know...** Some words do not have a plural form (for example, *money*, *milk*). Other words are always in the plural form (for example, *trousers*, *scissors*).

2. Look around you. Make a list of items you can see **more than one** of.

   books

3. Complete these sentences using **plurals**.

   a) Onto his ark Noah took: two _____ , two _____ ,

   two _____ and lots of other animals.

   b) At the market there were lots of things to buy: _____ ,

   _____ , _____ and many other things.

Pronouns

Pronouns are words we use **in place of nouns**. Words like *I*, *she*, *him* and *it* are all examples of pronouns. Pronouns are useful because they stop you from repeating the same words over and over again.

For example:

Jack tried to carry Jack's bag but Jack's bag was too heavy for Jack.

This sentence sounds strange because the same words are repeated. If pronouns are used the sentence sounds much better:

Jack tried to carry **his** bag but **it** was too heavy for **him**.

1. Here are some useful **pronouns**.

I me mine	he him his	she her hers	we us ours	they them their	it its

Rewrite these sentences using **pronouns** in place of the words in bold print.

a) Kavita and I went to the shop but **the shop** was closed.

_____

b) Mark had lost **Mark's** coat and could not find **the coat** anywhere.

_____

c) The twins were in the garden but **the twins'** mum did not see **the twins.**

_____

d) Nina knew that the book was **Nina's** but **Nina** did not want **the book**.

_____

e) The man was following **Mick and Me** and **Mick and I** were worried.

_____

f) Jordan thought **Jordan** had won the race, but **Jordan** should have looked behind **Jordan.**

_____

Did you know... One of the meanings of the prefix *pro-* is 'in place of'. So the word *pronoun* means 'in place of a noun'. This describes exactly what a pronoun does!

Pronouns are very useful, but sometimes we use too many of them. This can make our writing sound confusing.

For example: Carrie went to see Sophie. **She** was angry.

Here we are not sure whether it is Carrie or Sophie who is angry.

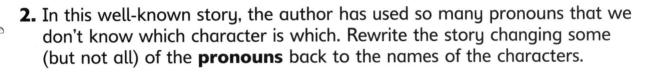

2. In this well-known story, the author has used so many pronouns that we don't know which character is which. Rewrite the story changing some (but not all) of the **pronouns** back to the names of the characters.

> **The tortoise and the hare waited for the gun to start the race. Bang! Immediately he flew out of the blocks. His long legs ate up the ground and soon he was completely out of sight. Meanwhile he had only just crossed the starting line. His little legs did not move very fast. Looking back from the top of the hill he saw him and laughed.**

_____

_____

_____

_____

_____

_____

Pronouns can be used to **make links between sentences**.

For example:

Sheena suggested we should go back. **This** seemed like a good idea.

The word **this** refers to Sheena's idea of going back.

3. What do the **pronouns** in these sentences refer to?

a) The old man opened the box. **It** was empty. (**It** = _the box_____)

b) Eric went first. I said **that** was not fair. (**that** = _____)

c) Nina won the race. **This** was a surprise. (**This** = _____)

d) Later we went to the disco. **It** was great. (**It** = _____)

Verbs

A **verb** is a **doing** or a **being** word. Verbs often tell us about actions – what someone or something is **doing**.

For example:
  The cat **sits**.   The frog **jumps**.   A door **opens**.   Jesse **stops**.

Some verbs tell us what someone or something **is** or **has**.
For example: I **have** black hair.   I **am** 10 years old.   We **are** tired.

1. Underline the **doing** or **action verbs** in each of these sentences.

  a) The aeroplane took off and soared into the sky.

  b) From behind a tree, the cat pounced suddenly.

  c) Carly listened for a moment before she stepped forward and spoke.

  d) Tigers often sleep by day and hunt at night.

2. Choose **verbs** from the box and add them to these sentences so that each of them makes sense.

  a) Mr Samuels _____ a frightening temper.

  b) Zebras _____ stripes.

  c) Paris _____ the capital city of France.

  d) Jamilla and Judith _____ twins.

  e) I _____ very happy today.

is
are
has
have
am

All **sentences** have to have a **verb** for them to make sense. Even the shortest sentence needs a verb.
For example: Raj **screamed**.   The car **crashed**.

3. Use the **nouns** and **verbs** from the boxes to make four short sentences.

  a) The _____

  b) A _____

  c) The _____

  d) _____

Nouns	Verbs
rain	laughed
building	groaned
Marcie	fell
king	shook

Verbs

The English language is full of interesting and exciting **verbs**, so don't make the mistake of choosing ordinary, boring verbs to use in your writing. **Powerful verbs** can suggest so much more about characters, moods and feelings.

For example: The old man **went** into the room.

'Went' is an ordinary, everyday verb. It does not tell us much about the character of the old man. If you change **went** to a more **powerful verb**, you can make sentences like:

The old man **danced** into the room. He was very happy.
The old man **stomped** into the room. He was very angry.
The old man **tip-toed** into the room. He shouldn't really have been there.

4. Change the boring everyday verb in each of these sentences for a more **powerful verb** that tells us something about the character.

a) The Princess **looked** _____ at the fisherman.

b) The giant **walked** _____ across the hillside.

c) The monster **ate** _____ his food.

d) The wind **went** _____ through the trees.

e) 'It's not fair,' **said** _____ Rashid.

f) The man **got** _____ into the car.

5. The verbs have been removed from this description of a storm. Write a **powerful verb** in each box to make the description sound effective.

Grey-black clouds [ ] across the sky. The branches on the

trees [ ] in the wind and the leaves [ ] all around.

Raindrops [ ] on the windowpane and [ ] in

puddles on the pavement. People [ ] down the road towards

their homes. They [ ] with their umbrellas in the rain.

Adverbs

Adverbs are words that give extra information about the events described in a sentence. A lot of adverbs give us information about **how** things happen (for example, *sadly, quickly, carefully*), but some adverbs tell us **where** (for example, *here, outside*) or **when** (for example, *today, tomorrow, always*).

For example:

The man was talking.   **Outside** the man was talking **cheerfully**.

The adverbs **outside** and **cheerfully** tell us more about this event.

1. Lots of **adverbs** that tell us **how** are formed by adding **–ly** to the end of adjectives. Add **–ly** to the end of these adjectives to make a collection of **adverbs**.

slow*ly*	anxious	sweet	peaceful	quiet	polite
loud	smart	careful	mad	cheerful	excited

2. Add an **adverb** to each of these short sentences to give more information about **how** the actions are performed. Use the **adverbs** you made above – or think of some of your own.

a) Ten children singing _____

b) Nine children dancing _____

c) Eight children reading _____

d) Seven children walking _____

e) Six children waiting _____

f) Five children talking _____

g) Four children laughing _____

h) Three children watching _____

i) Two children running _____

j) And just one child sleeping _____

Did you know...

A famous newspaper editor once claimed that there was no need to use adverbs. He said that the English language has so many wonderful verbs that it should always be possible to find exactly the right verb, without using an adverb at all. Why not try this out?! Before using an adverb, see if there is a powerful verb you can use instead.

A useful feature of **adverbs** is that they can be **moved** to different positions in a sentence. This means that you can decide which version of the sentence sounds the best.

For example: **Suddenly**, the wolf pounced.
The wolf pounced **suddenly**.
The wolf **suddenly** pounced.

3. Rewrite these sentences to include the **adverb** shown in the brackets. Decide where you think the **adverb** should be added – at the start, middle or end of the sentence.

a) The man spoke to his neighbours. (angrily)

_____

b) The Princess moved across the room. (gracefully)

_____

c) He walked along the plank. (carefully)

_____

d) He hid the letters under a book. (hurriedly)

_____

4. Rewrite these sentences so that they show the mood or feelings of the character mentioned. You can add **adverbs** or change the verbs for more powerful ones.

a) The king **got** to his feet and **went** out of the chamber.

_____

b) The woman **looked** around her as if she was **looking** for someone.

_____

c) Ed the elephant **took** the buns and **put** them into his mouth.

_____

d) The boy **ran** down the road **shouting**.

_____

Prepositions

Prepositions are little words that can be very useful for adding extra information into sentences. A lot of prepositions tell us **where** (for example, *on, in, under, over*) but some prepositions tell us **when** (for example, *before, after, during, on*).

For example: The old man waited **at** the bus stop **by** the post office.
This tells us **where** he was waiting.
The shop was broken into **during** the night.
This tells us **when** the shop was broken into.

1. Add a **prepositional phrase** to the end of these sentences to show **where** the events happened. Use **prepositions** from the box to help you.

a) The boy climbed *over the fence.*

b) The girl jumped _____

c) The man was standing _____

d) The car drove _____

e) The ghost appeared _____

f) Marcus fell _____

on
off
over
under
through
by
into
behind

Prepositional phrases that tell us **when** something happened can be **moved** to different places in a sentence.

For example: The game was over **by half time.**
By half time the game was over.

2. Add a **prepositional phrase** that tells us **when** each of these events happened. Choose a phrase from the box, or use one of your own. Don't forget to use a capital letter to start each sentence.

a) Sally went for a run _____

b) _____ it began to rain.

c) _____ all was quiet.

d) They couldn't go out _____

e) _____ we went to the cinema.

at midnight
before breakfast
during the night
on Saturday
after tea

Prepositions

Although they are only little words, **prepositions** are very important. Changing a preposition can totally change the meaning of a sentence.

For example: The car drove **through** the water.
The car drove **by** the water.
The car drove **under** the water!

Each of these sentences gives a completely different picture of the event.

3. Change the meaning of each of these sentences by changing the **preposition**. Write the new version of each sentence on the line.

a) The cat was sitting **by** the box.   *The cat was sitting in the box.*

b) The path went **behind** the wood. _____

c) The boy scrambled **through** the hedge. _____

d) Sophie walked **by** the river. _____

e) George was hiding **in** the dustbin. _____

f) They arrived home **during** tea. _____

4. Make each of these recipe instructions more precise by adding one of the **prepositional phrases** from the box.

a) Mix the flour and sugar together _____ .

b) Heat the butter and milk _____ .

c) Roll out the mixture _____ .

d) Place the biscuits _____ .

e) Take the biscuits out of the oven _____ .

f) Leave them to cool _____ .

after 20 minutes	**before** tasting	**in** a large bowl
on a baking tray	**over** a low heat	**with** a rolling pin

Connectives and conjunctions

Connectives are words and phrases that help to **link together** ideas. Some connectives link together ideas **within a sentence** – these are called **conjunctions** (see page 20). Other connectives link together ideas in **separate sentences** or paragraphs.

For example: Cinderella was delighted with the beautiful dress. **However**, it still did not help her to get to the ball.
▲
The word *however* is a **connective** that links the ideas in these two sentences.

I. Different **connectives** link ideas together in different ways. Underline the **connective** that best links the ideas in each pair of sentences.

a) The children were hoping to go to the beach. | **Also, However,** | it rained all day.

b) It was snowing heavily this morning. | **As a result, Finally,** | lots of people were late for school.

c) We visited the famous landmarks in Paris. | **Next, For example,** | we went to the Eiffel Tower.

d) Our train was over an hour late. | **Eventually, Before** | we arrived at our destination.

e) The trainers were not really what I wanted. | **Also, Finally** | they were too expensive.

f) It was fine all day today. | **Because, In contrast,** | it rained all yesterday.

2. Connectives are useful when giving a point of view on a subject. Write a second sentence that fits with each of these **connectives**.

a) Many people need to use their cars every day. **For example,**

_____

b) Many people need to use their cars every day. **However,**

_____

c) Many people need to use their cars every day. **As a result,**

_____

d) Many people need to use their cars every day. **After all,**

_____

Connectives and conjunctions

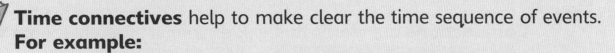

Time connectives help to make clear the time sequence of events. **For example:**

next	later	meanwhile	suddenly
after that	now	at that moment	finally

3. Here are the main events from the story of Red Riding Hood. Add a **time connective** before each event to show the time sequence of the events. Don't use the word *then*.

a) Red Riding Hood was walking through the forest.

b) _____ a wolf jumped out and surprised her.

c) _____ Red Riding Hood went on her way again.

d) _____ the wolf rushed to Granny's house.

e) _____ Red Riding Hood arrived at Granny's house.

f) _____ the wolf tried to eat Red Riding Hood!

g) _____ a woodcutter rushed in and killed the wolf.

h) _____ everyone was safe.

Cause and effect connectives are used to help explain something clearly. They show how one event causes or leads to another.

For example: The sun came out. **As a result** the washing dried quickly.

4. Complete the second sentence to show what might happen as a result of the event described in the first sentence. The **cause and effect connectives** are shown in bold.

a) It has not rained for several weeks.
Consequently _____

b) The wind fills the sails of the yacht.
As a result _____

c) The handles on the bag were not very strong.
Therefore _____

d) The lions had not eaten for some time.
Because of this _____

Connectives and conjunctions

Conjunctions are words that link or connect together ideas **within a sentence**. Words like *because, while, so, although* are all examples of conjunctions. They help us to form **complex sentences** (see page 36).

For example:

The tortoise plodded on **until** he found the hare asleep under the tree.

first idea   conjunction   second idea

5. Choose a **conjunction** from the box to complete these sentences.

unless	as	although	because	when	since

a) The old man continued on his way _____ it was getting dark.

b) Do not enter the room _____ a green light is showing.

c) Everyone rushed towards the river _____ the fire spread out of control.

d) He fell asleep in his chair _____ he was so tired.

e) _____ he saw the food, he gobbled it up immediately.

6. Different **conjunctions** link ideas in different ways. Write an ending for each sentence to fit with the **conjunction** given.

a) The monster roared loudly **when**

_____

b) The monster roared loudly **because**

_____

c) The monster roared loudly **although**

_____

d) The monster roared loudly **until**

_____

e) The monster roared loudly **so**

_____

f) The monster roared loudly **if**

_____

Revision of word classes

We have now looked at the different types, or **classes**, of words. This page will help you to check your understanding of the different classes and show you how words fit together.

Here are some of the main **classes of words** we have looked at so far.

noun	adjective	verb
adverb	preposition	conjunction

1. What **class** or type of word is missing from each of these sentences? Write the **class** of word in the box. The first one has been done for you.

   a) The [adjective] elephant lumbered down to the watering hole.

   b) Slowly, the old [   ] shuffled along the street.

   c) The fearful child [   ] anxiously to its mother

   d) The grand old gentleman waited patiently [   ] the hallway.

   e) The lion [   ] stalked its prey.

   f) The waves became stronger [   ] the wind whipped the surface of the sea.

2. Write examples of words from the different **classes** to make chain sentences.

	adjective	noun	verb	prepositional phrase
a) The	chattering	monkey	swings	through the trees.
b) An				
c) The				
d) A				
e) The				
f) A				

It is important to **choose the right words** if you want to make your writing effective and interesting. You might need to rethink your choice of words when you are revising and editing your work. Ask yourself:

Are these the best possible words?
Do these words say exactly what I want them to say?

If not, choose a better word. For example, the writer of this story has decided to change some of the words in this sentence to make the event more exciting:

> *Suddenly   sprang   huge   razor fangs*
> ~~Then~~/~~out~~/~~jumped~~ a/~~big~~ monster with/~~sharp~~/~~teeth~~.

1. Improve this description by making the setting sound more impressive. Try changing or adding, **nouns**, **adjectives**, **verbs** and **adverbs** as in the example above.

Two big gold doors opened to show the lovely ballroom. The room

was very long and full of people, all dancing. The walls were

all white and the ceiling was patterned. There were lovely red curtains

hanging at the windows. The floor was made of stone. Right at the end

of the ballroom were two big, gold chairs standing on a platform.

2. Try making this extract from a story sound more exciting by improving the choice of words.

Casper ran forward and took the burning torch from the wall.

The dragon turned round and looked at him. Casper waved

the torch at the dragon. The dragon put his head back and

roared. Smoke came out of his nose and flames came out

of his mouth. The hot breath made Casper go back.

Did you know...
The word *text* comes from the Latin word *texere*, which means 'to weave'. Writing is choosing rich and colourful words and then weaving them together to produce the finished text.

Editing and Revising 1 – Word Choice

Sometimes you will find the opposite problem to that described on page 22. We get carried away and use too many words. We use too many **adjectives**, or use **adverbs** when really we should just choose a better **verb**. After you have finished a piece of writing, decide whether all the words you have used are really needed, or whether there are times when you could use one word in place of three.

For example: Sam was feeling bright, ~~happy, jolly~~ and cheerful

strolled   lane

as he ~~walked happily~~ down the ~~little, narrow~~ road.

3. Edit this text. **Replace** each group of words that has been crossed out with just one **verb**.

Prince Fortune ~~walked with big strides~~ into the hall. He ~~had a quick look~~ across the room to where the Queen and Princess were ~~talking really quietly~~ together.

4. In this text, too many **adjectives** have been used.
Cross out any **adjectives** that are not really needed.

Three butterflies danced together in the bright, dazzling, glorious early morning sunshine. They fluttered their vivid, bright, vibrant, colourful wings as they danced their merry, graceful, clever dance of friendship. The three butterflies were always happy, cheerful and merry to be together. But just then a big, horrible, threatening, dark rain cloud passed in front of the bright, dazzling, glorious sun.

5. Using the right words in non-fiction writing is very important. Choose a word from the box to replace the words that have been crossed out.

a) Too much sugar can ~~make~~ teeth ~~rot~~.

b) A telescope is ~~a thing~~ that makes ~~far away~~ objects seem nearer.

c) The Moon ~~goes round~~ the Earth.

orbits
distant
cause
to decay
an instrument

Editing and Revising 2 – Word Order

As well as thinking about which words you use, you also need to think about how you organise them. Remember that some words, such as **adverbs** and **prepositional phrases**, can be moved around within a sentence.

For example, imagine a writer has written the sentence:

The shadowy figure crept **across the garden cautiously**.

When reading through this sentence later, the writer decides that it sounds awkward. He or she tries moving the adverb and the prepositional phrase around and comes up with different possibilities:

Across the garden the shadowy figure crept **cautiously**.
or **Cautiously**, the shadowy figure crept **across the garden**.
or The shadowy figure crept **cautiously across the garden**.

1. Rewrite these sentences moving the **adverbs** and/or the **prepositional phrase**. Try out ideas in your head to see which version sounds the best.

a) **Out of the window** the Princess threw the bottle **carelessly**.

_____

b) The villagers were **anxiously** waiting **at midnight**.

_____

c) The explorers went without any food **frequently during this time**.

_____

d) He was in trouble **at school usually**.

_____

2. Arrange these words and phrases to make three different versions of the sentence.

| he strode | purposefully | through the town |

a) _____

b) _____

c) _____

Here are some writing projects that you can try at home. Each project lets you focus on using a particular class of words.

Keep a diary

Keep a diary and write about all the things you do. Make sure that you use the right **pronouns** to refer to your friends (*they*), you and your family (*we*) and yourself (*I*). Remember, don't use too many **pronouns** or when you read it back you won't know who did what!

Shopping lists

Write a list of things you want to buy when you go shopping. Think about the **nouns** you use and be precise. For example, instead of writing *shoes*, decide on the sort of shoes you want – trainers, boots... Count how many **plurals** you have used on your list. Have you used any **proper nouns**?

Send a card

Why wait for birthdays to send a special card to your friends and relations? You can send **superlative** cards at any time to tell people how special they are. For example, make a card for your most helpful/ kindest/ funniest/ cleverest friend. Design it yourself and write a special **superlative** message.

An argument for...

Impress your parents by writing an argument explaining why you deserve extra pocket money, a mobile phone for your birthday or something else that you would like to have. Use **connectives** such as *Firstly, Moreover, Furthermore, for example, Although, In conclusion* to help make your argument sound impressive.

List of things to do

At the start of the weekend, make a list of things to do. Look at the **verbs** that you have used. You have probably used lots of ordinary **verbs** such as *go, do, take*... Try to think of a better verb to use in each case. For example, instead of *Do homework*, write *Complete homework*.

Fun and games

Play the **powerful verb** game with your friends. This is like the game of charades but you have to mime interesting **verbs** rather than titles. Start by writing some really interesting **verbs** on separate pieces of paper. Fold them up and then ask your friends to pick one out and mime it.

Verb tenses

The word *tense* refers to *when* something happens. Verbs can be in the **past**, **present** or **future** tense. If something has already happened, you use the **past tense**. If it is happening right at this moment, you use the **present tense**. If it is yet to happen, you use the **future tense**.

For example:

Yesterday I **played** outside.   **past tense** – it has already happened
I **play** outside.   **present tense** – it is happening now
Tomorrow I **shall play** outside.   **future tense** – it has yet to happen

1. These sentences are written in the **present tense**. Rewrite each sentence, changing the verb to the **past tense** as if the event has already happened.

   a) It **is** hot today.   ▶ It was hot last week.

   b) I **hear** a strange sound. ▶ _____

   c) I **jump** high.   ▶ _____

   d) I **take** my time.   ▶ _____

   e) Ed **runs** for the bus.   ▶ _____

2. Rewrite these sentences, changing the verb to the **future tense** as if the event has yet to happen.

   a) It **is** hot today.   ▶ It will be hot tomorrow.

   b) Jill **is** late today.   ▶ _____

   c) I **help** to wash-up.   ▶ _____

   d) We **have** our breakfast at eight o'clock. ▶ _____

3. Here is an event from the middle of a well-known story. Write a sentence about what happened earlier (use the **past tense**) and a sentence about what will happen later (use the **future tense**).

   a) Earlier _____

   b) At the moment Goldilocks **is** asleep in the three bears' cottage.

   c) Later _____

4. This commentary on a sporting event is in the present tense.
Rewrite it in the **past tense** as if you were reporting what happened.

> Johnston **crosses** from the left. A shot **comes** in from Liddell. It **bounces** off a defender. Liddell **fires** the ball back towards goal, but the goalkeeper **saves** easily.

Johnston crossed _____

_____

_____

_____

_____

_____

5. The **future tense** is used when talking about events that are yet to happen. Write a horoscope making predictions about what might happen for people born under the star sign Leo during the week ahead.

Leo

In the week ahead you **will meet** many new and interesting people.

_____

_____

Did you know...? The English language has no future tense. Of course, that doesn't stop us from talking and writing about things that have yet to happen. We use other verbs such as *will, shall, am/are going to* with the main verb.

For example: On Saturday **we are going** on holiday. We **will be leaving** early.

First, second and third person

First person is when the writer speaks about himself or herself (using the words *I... We...*); **second person** is when the writer speaks to the reader (*You...*); **third person** is when the writer speaks about someone or something else (using the words *they..., he..., she..., it...*). Notice how the **verbs** and **pronouns** change in these examples.

For example: **I am** late. first person – the writer speaks about him/herself

You are late. second person – the writer speaks directly to the reader

He is late. third person – the writer speaks about someone else

1. Read each of these sentences. Write a label to show whether it is written in:

first person	second person	third person

a) My name is Louise and I live in Cardiff.

b) The children tried to keep up, but they were tired.

c) Venus is the second planet in the Solar System.

d) To play this game you will need a football.

e) I could not see because of the mist.

2. Below you can read what Lucy has written about herself. Rewrite the information about Lucy using the **third person**.

I am 11 years old and I go to Midfield School in Stonington. When I grow up I would like to be a singer and have a hit CD.

Lucy is 11 years old and _____

_____

_____

_____

_____

_____

First, second and third person

Stories can be written in the **first** or **third person**. A first person story sounds like one of the characters is telling the story.

3. Here is an extract from a story that is written in the **third person**. Rewrite the story as if it were written in the **first person** – as if the fisherman were telling the story.

> The fisherman had been working all day, but still he had not caught one fish. He pulled up the last of his nets – it was empty, like all the others. The fisherman thought how unlucky he was. What would he tell his children? Just then, something in the water caught his eye. The fisherman looked over the side of the boat to get a better look...

I had been working all day, _____

_____

_____

_____

_____

_____

_____

_____

Did you know...? In Elizabethan times the endings of verbs were very different to those we use today. Second person verbs would end with –st or –est, for example: *canst, dost, playest, hearest.* Third person verbs would end with –th or –eth, for example: *goeth, saith.*

Here are some lines from the play *A Midsummer Night's Dream*, written by William Shakespeare. Look at the different verb endings:

    Demetrius: Where is Lysander and fair Hermia?

                The one **I'll slay, the other slayeth** me.

                Thou told'st me they were stolen unto this wood...

Agreement

Verbs sometimes change depending on the **person** you are writing about.

For example:

I have two brothers.   **He has** two brothers.

I am 10 years old.   **She is** 10 years old.   **They are** 10 years old.

I play the guitar.   **He plays** the guitar.

Choosing the right verb is easy if you say the sentence in your head before writing it down. If you choose the wrong form of the verb, it sounds strange.

For example:

I has two brothers.   **He am** 10 years old.   **I plays** the guitar.

1. Check the verbs in these sentences. Put a tick in the box if the verb is right, put a cross if the wrong form of the verb has been chosen.

a) I plays for the school team. ☐

d) They am waiting for the bus. ☐

b) We were really pleased. ☐

e) You have five more minutes. ☐

c) I has some money to spend. ☐

f) I hates cheese and onion crisps. ☐

2. You should have found four sentences where the wrong verb has been chosen. Rewrite these four sentences using the correct verb.

_____

_____

_____

_____

3. Make sentences by choosing the correct form of the verb from the box.

a) You _____ happy.

b) She _____ lots of friends.

c) I _____ pleased.

d) They _____ a beautiful house.

e) He _____ tired.

are
is
am
has
have

Editing and Revising 3 – Grammatical Accuracy

When we are writing there are a lot of things to remember. It is easy to forget which **tense** or **person** you are writing in. This is why it is important that you read through your writing and check that everything **makes sense** and **sounds right**.

1. Read through this piece of writing. The writer was working so quickly that he missed out some words. Put in the missing words so that the writing makes sense.

On Saturday we went $\overset{to}{\wedge}$ watch the school football team play in the

Player's Cup. It a very exciting game. The final score was 2–2, was

probably a fair result because both teams played well. Our team scored

first, thanks to magnificent free kick from Lee Edwards. But then they

equalised just before the whistle went half time.

2. Check the **verbs** that have been used in this piece of writing. Change any **verbs** that do not sound right.

Let me tell you about my family. We $\overset{live}{\cancel{lives}}$ in a house on the corner of Grant

Street. I has two sisters and a brother. My sisters is twins. My brother is

older than me. Sometimes we all plays together, but sometimes we argue.

Did you know... Grammar rules, like using the correct form of a verb, were only fixed in the seventeenth and eighteenth centuries. At that time, it was decided that there should be a Standard English, which everyone would follow. We still use the term Standard English today. It is the sort of English we usually use when we are writing. In spoken language, however, Standard English is just one version of English. People from different parts of Britain and in different parts of the world have different ways of saying things. In some parts of the country it is perfectly normal to say 'I seen him', although people would still write the standard form – 'I saw him'.

Simple sentences

A **sentence** is a group of words that are put together to **say something**. A sentence must always **make sense**. If it does not make sense, then it is not a sentence. Sentences can be very short or they can be very long. A **simple sentence** has just one thing to say.

For example: The dragon ran away.

Simple sentences can be made longer by adding **adjectives**, **adverbs** and **prepositions** that give extra information about the event.

For example:
Fearfully, the **little** dragon ran away **from the smoking mountain**.

1. Here are some parts of sentences. Make each one into a complete **sentence**.

    a) the angry lion ▶ <u>The angry lion glared through the bars of the cage.</u>

    b) pieces on the floor ▶ _____

    c) two pointed ears ▶ _____

    d) on the way to school ▶ _____

    e) the excited children ▶ _____

2. For a sentence to make sense it must have a verb. Read the sentences you have written in Activity 1 and underline the **verb** in each **sentence**. For example: *The angry lion <u>glared</u> through the bars of the cage.*

3. Select a **verb** from the box to help make each of these phrases into a **sentence**. Add some words of your own to complete the **sentence**.

    a) The horse *trotted down the road.*

    b) The rock climbers _____

    c) The wizard _____

    d) A butterfly _____

    e) A dog _____

fluttered
trotted
vanished
barked
clambered

The **order of words** in a **sentence** is important.

For example, saying:

The man caught a large fish.

is not the same as saying...

A large fish caught the man.

4. Reorder the words in these sentences so that they make sense.

a) The sports car drove the man. ▶ *The man drove the sports car.*

b) His breakfast ate the boy. ▶ _____

c) Screamed out of the window the child. ▶ _____

d) A robot made the inventor. ▶ _____

e) The television watched Tarik. ▶ _____

5. Sometimes when we are reading we make short notes. Later we can change these notes back into full sentences. Rewrite these short notes as full sentences.

a) Charles Dickens, born 1812 ▶ *Charles Dickens was born in 1812.*

b) James Watt, inventor ▶ _____

c) Gorillas, largest of apes ▶ _____

d) Polar bears, the Arctic ▶ _____

e) Today, sunny ▶ _____

Did you know...? The word *sentence* comes from the Latin word *sententia*, which originally meant 'feeling'. The word was later used to describe all sorts of feelings, opinions, judgements and ideas. Eventually it came to mean expressing these ideas *in words*, which is where our modern word *sentence* comes from.

Phrases and clauses

Longer **sentences** are made up of **phrases** and **clauses**. A **clause** is a group of words that includes a verb – it usually tells you about an event (see page 38). A **phrase** is a group of words that does not contain a verb – it gives extra information about an event in a sentence.

A **simple sentence** can be made more interesting by adding **phrases**. **For example:**

Once there lived a wise man.
Once, **in a far and distant land**, there lived a wise man **with three daughters**.

▲

The extra phrases give more information about the setting and the man.

1. Choose **phrases** from the box to add to the start and end of these simple sentences. You can use a **phrase** more than once if you want to.

with the class	in a car	just a moment later
in the morning	in the corridor	only the other day

a) _____ the teacher was furious _____

b) _____ the robber escaped _____

c) _____ a boy slipped over _____

Clauses also add extra information into a **sentence**.
For example:
Gregory took charge of the money. (He was the oldest.)
Gregory, who was the oldest, took charge of the money.

2. Rewrite these sentences adding the information from the brackets.

a) Paula refused to move. (she was exhausted)

Paula, _____ , refused to move.

b) Mr King was now very late. (he had left early)

Mr King, _____ , was now very late.

c) The beggar pleaded for help. (he was blind)

The beggar, _____ , pleaded for help.

Compound sentences

A **compound sentence** is made when you **join two simple sentences** together. A connecting word (or **conjunction**) like *and*, *but* or *so* is used to join the sentences.

For example:

It was becoming dark. Joe was beginning to worry.

These two simple sentences can be joined together to make:

It was becoming dark **and** Joe was beginning to worry.

1. Rewrite each pair of sentences as a **compound sentence**. Use one of these words to join the sentences together.

and	**but**	**so**	**or**

a) I missed the bus. I wasn't late.

_____

b) The windows were open. Everyone could hear him singing.

_____

c) He picked up all the rubbish. He put it in the bin.

_____

d) It will be dry in the north. There will be rain in the south.

_____

e) We could go to the zoo. We could go into town.

_____

2. Complete these **compound sentences**.

a) The car stopped **and** _____

b) The car stopped **but** _____

c) Jack was bored **so** _____

d) Jack was bored **and** _____

e) Simone loved to play football **but** _____

f) Simone loved to play football **so** _____

Complex sentences

Complex sentences link two or more ideas together within one sentence. Sometimes **conjunctions** are used to link the ideas; sometimes **verbs** are used.

For example, here are two ideas, in two separate sentences:
 The man opened the door to his house. He was pleased to be home.

These ideas can be linked to make one **complex sentence**.
For example:
 The man opened the door to his house, **pleased** to be home.
 Pleased to be home, the man opened the door to his house.
 As the man opened the door to his house, he was pleased to be home.

The first two examples use the verb **pleased** as the linking word, while the third example uses the conjunction **as**. Commas help to separate the two parts of the sentence.

1. Make five different **complex sentences** using the **simple sentences** and **conjunctions** shown in the box. One sentence has been done for you.

I went straight to bed.   when   I was feeling miserable.
It was dark.   as   I ran away.   We arrived home.   because

a) As it was dark, I went straight to bed.

b) _____

c) _____

d) _____

e) _____

2. Link these ideas into a **complex sentence**. Use the verb from the first of the two sentences in each pair.

a) Ellen stood by the door. She watched the storm approaching.

 Standing by the door, _____

b) The man was waving his arms madly. He shouted for help.

 _____

c) The car was travelling fast. It just missed the approaching lorry.

 _____

Schofield & Sims | Understanding Englis

Complex sentences

If you use too many **simple sentences** your writing may sound jerky rather than smooth and flowing.

For example:
Visham ate his breakfast. He went to the park.
He went to meet his friend Nick.

All this information is better combined in one **complex sentence**:

Having eaten his breakfast, Visham went to the park to meet his friend Nick.

3. Combine the information from each series of **simple sentences** into one **complex sentence**.

a) The sun began to rise. The grey world became lighter. The birds awoke from their sleep.

_____

_____

b) Lee was feeling confident. He climbed straight to the top of the ladder. He did not look down.

_____

_____

c) The sloth is a slow-moving mammal. It has long hair. It lives in trees.

_____

_____

d) He walked quickly. He followed the mysterious figure. They went through the marketplace.

_____

_____

e) The waves wash over the rocks. The rocks are worn away. The rocks become smooth.

_____

_____

Main and subordinate clauses

Complex sentences are made up of at least two parts, or **clauses**. One part is the **main clause**. The **main clause** makes sense by itself. The other part is the **subordinate clause**. The **subordinate clause** gives extra information. It does not make sense if you read it without the main clause.

For example: The man became angry when no-one would let him in.

             the main clause   the subordinate clause

Screaming wildly, she ran from the house.

        the subordinate clause   the main clause

1. Read these complex sentences. Draw a <u>solid line</u> under the **main clause** and draw a <u>broken line</u> under the **subordinate clause**.

a) The dog snarled at her, growling menacingly.

b) With his heart pounding, Dean stepped forward.

c) While she was reading, the doorbell rang.

d) The lights came on one at a time until the whole street was lit up.

e) When the factory closed, many people lost their jobs.

f) Stretch the fabric over the card, folding the edges under neatly.

2. The **subordinate clause** can be added at the beginning or end of the sentence. Rewrite these sentences, moving the **subordinate clause** to the start of the sentence.

a) Everything was quiet until the storm began.

_____

b) The man strolled along the street humming merrily.

_____

c) The match was still a draw despite playing extra time.

_____

Effective writing uses a mixture of **simple**, **compound** and **complex** sentences. **Simple sentences** are clear and to the point, but too many will make your writing sound jerky. **Complex sentences** link ideas together and make writing flow, but if they are too complex, they will sound confusing. Always use a mixture of different kinds of sentence.

I. This paragraph uses only simple sentences. See if you can improve it by turning some of the sentences into **compound** and **complex** ones.

One day Phil and Leon went to the canal. They were going fishing. There seemed to be no-one else around. They chose the best place. They started to get out the rods. Then there was a loud splash. Then there was a scream. Phil and Leon looked up. They saw something moving in the water. Then they saw a hand waving. Someone had fallen into the water.

2. This next extract is all one sentence. See if you can improve it by splitting it into **separate sentences**.

Like all animals, human beings need food in order to live because every part of the body needs a steady supply of food so that it can work properly, but first the food has to be broken down through a process called digestion so that it can dissolve in the blood and travel around the body.

Sentence construction has gone through many changes in fashion. In the eighteenth and nineteenth centuries, long complex sentences were all the rage! For example, this is the first sentence from Robert Louis Stevenson's novel *Treasure Island*:

Squire Trelawney, Dr Livesey, and the rest of these gentlemen having asked me to write down the whole particulars about Treasure Island, from the beginning to the end, keeping nothing back but the bearings of the island, and that only because there is still treasure not yet lifted, I take up my pen in the year of grace 17--, and go back to the time when my father kept the 'Admiral Benbow' inn, and the brown old seaman, with the sabre cut, first took up his lodging under our roof.

That's all one sentence! Luckily, the fashion now is for shorter and simpler sentences!

Sentence types

Some sentences are **statements**, some are **questions** and some are **instructions or commands**. By making small changes you can quite easily change the type of sentence you are writing.

For example: **You are** going to school. ◀ a statement
Are you going to school? ◀ a question
Go to school. ◀ a command or instruction

By changing **the order of words**, a question is made. By bringing the verb to the beginning of the sentence, a direct command is formed.

1. Use the words in the box to make a **statement** and then a **question**.

a)
| planning a holiday |
| you are . ? |

Statement: You are planning a holiday.

Question: Are you planning a holiday?

b)
| cold is it . ? |

Statement: _____

Question: _____

c)
| bored you are . ? |

Statement: _____

Question: _____

d)
| help me you |
| can . ? |

Statement: _____

Question: _____

2. Take each **statement** and rewrite it as a **command** (or **instruction**).

a) Statement: We take the dog for a walk every day.
Command: Take the dog for a walk every day.

b) Statement: We are going to visit Hammington Hall this weekend.
Command: _____

c) Statement: We always eat lots of fruit and vegetables.
Command: _____

d) Statement: We always stack the chairs neatly.
Command: _____

3. Turn these **questions** into direct **commands**.

a) Could you help me? ▶ *Help me.* _____

b) Can you hold this end? ▶ _____

c) Do you want to try this? ▶ _____

d) Have you tried this new ice cream? ▶ _____

e) Will you come and visit soon? ▶ _____

4. You can make your writing sound lively and interesting by using different types of sentences. Read this advert for Supakleena. Label the **statement**, the **question** and the **command**.

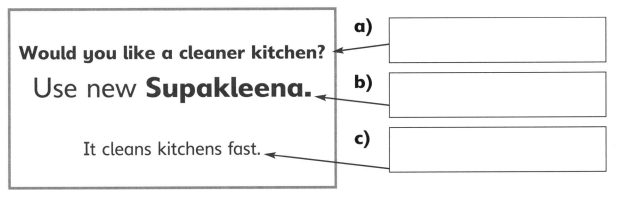

Would you like a cleaner kitchen?

Use new **Supakleena.**

It cleans kitchens fast.

a) _____

b) _____

c) _____

5. Try designing and writing an advert for a new computer game. Use at least **one statement**, **one question** and **one command**.

Did you know... Grammar is constantly changing to fit new situations. Think about e-mails and text messages. In text messages you don't use sentences. Instead you use phrases, shortened forms and even abbreviations.

For example: How you?   Great time Saturday!   CU

Positive and negative sentences

Sentences can be **positive** or **negative**.
For example:

I **like** peanut butter. ◀ positive   I **do not like** peanut butter. ◀ negative

Everyone likes peanut butter. ◀ positive   **Nobody** likes peanut butter. ◀ negative

Negative sentences use words such as **not**, **never**, **nobody** and **nothing**.

1. Complete this chart to show **positive** and **negative** versions of these sentences. The first one has been done for you.

	Positive	Negative
a)	Drop litter on the floor.	Do not drop litter on the floor.
b)	Everybody can help.	
c)		We cannot save the planet.
d)	Everything is finished.	
e)	We always go swimming on Mondays.	

2. Complete these sentences so that the first part is **positive** and the second part is **negative**.

a) I can <u>swim</u> , but I **never** <u>swim in the sea.</u>

b) I can _____, but I can**not** _____

c) I did _____, but I did **not** _____

d) Lots of people _____, but **nobody** _____

Be careful not to use **two negative words** in a sentence.
For example:

I **never** said **nothing**. ◀ This suggests that you **did** say **something**.

3. Write the correct version of each of these sentences.

a) I never said n̶o̶t̶h̶i̶n̶g̶. *I never said anything.*

b) Nobody did nothing to help. _____

c) I never saw nobody. _____

d) I don't like nothing here. _____

Conditional sentences

A **conditional sentence** has two parts or clauses. One part of the sentence depends on the events or situation described in the other part of the sentence.

For example: If it is sunny at the weekend, **then** we will go camping.

first part of the sentence | second part of the sentence

They will only go camping **if** the event described in the first part of the sentence actually happens.

Lots of conditional sentences use the word **if**. You will also find words like *then, might, could, would* in conditional sentences.

1. Complete these **conditional sentences** by adding a second part that says what you would or might do in each situation.

a) If it is sunny at the weekend, I _____

b) If I were famous, I _____

c) If I won the lottery, I _____

d) If I worked hard, I _____

e) If I had a magic carpet, _____

f) If I ruled the world, _____

2. Conditional sentences are useful for suggesting what might happen in the future. Complete these **conditional sentences**.

a) If we continue to destroy forests, _____

b) If everyone drops litter in the street, _____

c) If everyone switched off one light, _____

d) If Jack decides to climb the beanstalk, _____

e) If they cannot escape from the dragon's cave, _____

Did you know... Conditional sentences can be used to *look forward* to what might happen, or to *look back* on what caused things to happen. The poet and writer Rudyard Kipling once wrote a poem called *If*. The poem is like one long conditional sentence and uses the word *If* 13 times!

Direct and reported speech

There are two ways of writing down what someone says: you can use **direct speech** or **reported speech**.
Direct speech is when you write down exactly what the person said. You use speech marks to show the beginning and end of the spoken words.

For example: 'I have no-one to help me,' said Mrs Chatterjee.

Reported speech is when you write what has been said but you do not use the exact words spoken – instead you report it in your own words.

For example: Mrs Chatterjee said that she had no-one to help her.

1. Write these exchanges as **direct speech**.
Put speech marks around the words that are actually spoken. Start a new line each time a new character starts to speak. You can choose the names for the characters.

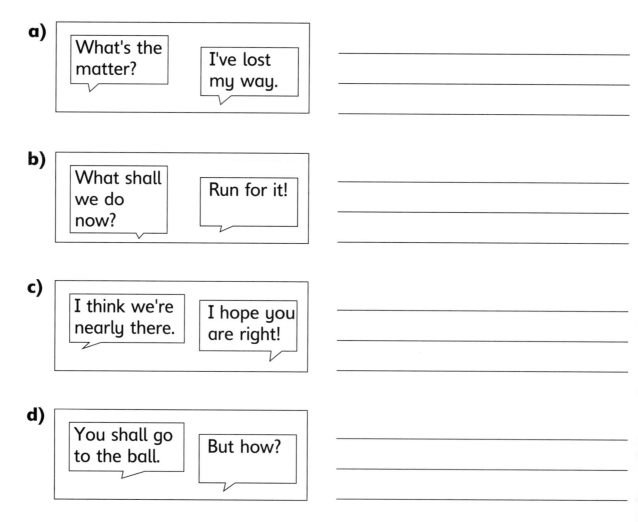

a)

What's the matter?

I've lost my way.

_____
_____
_____

b)

What shall we do now?

Run for it!

_____
_____
_____

c)

I think we're nearly there.

I hope you are right!

_____
_____
_____

d)

You shall go to the ball.

But how?

_____
_____
_____

Direct and reported speech

You will often need to write down what people say when you are writing stories or newspaper reports. It is a good idea to use some **direct** and some **reported speech**.

2. Change these examples of **direct speech** into **reported speech**.

a) 'I know the answer!' shouted Judith suddenly.

_____

b) 'Can we follow our footsteps back through the forest?' asked Michael.

_____

c) 'The dog must have buried the key in the garden,' explained George.

_____

d) 'It's all my fault,' said Rebecca.

_____

3. You are writing a newspaper report about a disastrous holiday. Write down what these people said about their holiday using reported speech.

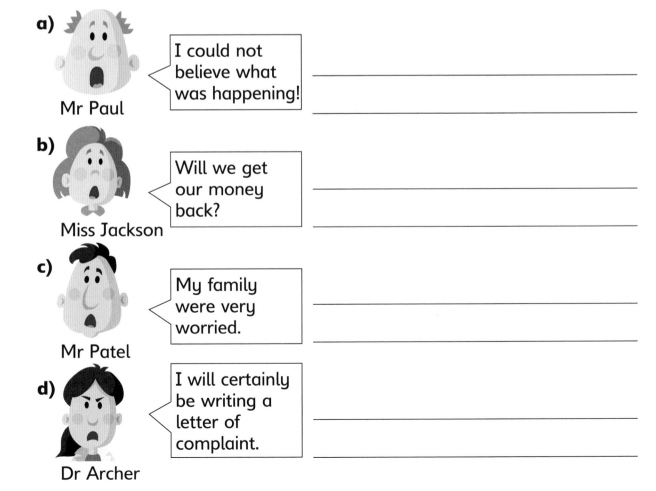

a) Mr Paul — I could not believe what was happening!

b) Miss Jackson — Will we get our money back?

c) Mr Patel — My family were very worried.

d) Dr Archer — I will certainly be writing a letter of complaint.

Active and passive

Active and **passive** versions of a sentence say the same thing in different ways.

For example: The pirates **hid** the treasure. ◀ active
The treasure **was hidden** by the pirates. ◀ passive

In the **passive sentence** the words have been moved around. This sentence is about what happens to the treasure, rather than being about the actions of the pirates. The **verb** changes from the **active form (hid)** to the **passive form (was hidden)**.

1. Change these active sentences into **passive sentences**.

a) The children put on a play.

▶ *A play was put on by the children.*

b) Everybody enjoyed the show.

▶

c) A fire destroyed the factory.

▶

d) A whistle silenced the crowd.

▶

e) The sudden noise surprised Fatima.

▶

2. Continue these **passive** sentences to reveal **who** was responsible for the events.

a) The plate was broken by

▶

b) The bag of gold was stolen by

▶

c) The man was hurt by

▶

d) The car was damaged by

▶

e) The lion was captured by

▶

Active and passive

In a **passive sentence** you can hide the 'doer' of the action. This is useful when you do not know who it is or when it is not important.

For example: I **connected** the wires to the battery. ◀ **active**
The wires **were connected** to the battery. by me ◀ **passive**
— **who** did it is probably not important, so it can be left out of the sentence

3. Change the following sentences to the **passive form** and hide the person doing the actions.

a) People used pigeons to send messages.

▶ *Pigeons were used to send messages.*

b) Someone annoyed the headteacher.

▶

c) We sent the letter to the Prime Minister.

▶

d) Someone stole the pirates' treasure.

▶

e) I asked the people for their opinions.

▶

4. In these sentences the **person** doing the action is **not important**. Write the sentences in the passive form.

a) We watered the plants every day.

▶ *The plants were watered every day.*

b) Joe invited the Mayor to the show.

▶

c) We attached the wires to the battery.

▶

d) Kavita added salt to the water.

▶

e) The class discussed a lot of ideas.

▶

Now you try 2!

Here are some more writing projects that you can try at home. Each project will help you focus on using some of your knowledge about grammar.

Write a letter to a friend

Write a letter to a friend or relative you have not seen for some time.
Write a lot of things about yourself (using **first person**). Write some news about other people or things that have been happening locally (use **third person**). Write some things directly to your reader (use **second person**).

Keep a scrapbook

Keep a scrapbook to remind yourself of special places, people or events. Include photographs, cuttings, leaflets and pictures. Write captions to explain each item. Write one **simple sentence**, one **compound sentence** and one **complex sentence** for each entry in your scrapbook.

Send a postcard

When you go on holiday write a postcard to a friend. Write about something you did yesterday (use the **past tense**), what you are doing at that moment (use the **present tense**) and what you are planning to do the next day (use the **future tense**).

Advert

Look closely at adverts in magazines or on the television. Look for examples of different **types of sentences** – particularly **questions** and **commands**. Have a go at writing your own advertisements using the same sorts of sentence.

What if...

This is a good way of exercising your imagination. Start with a blank piece of paper. Try to think of a really unusual situation (for example, if you shrank in the rain). Then think of all the things that might happen if that event actually occurred. Write your ideas down as **conditional sentences**. Fill the piece of paper with amazing possibilities.

Star reporter

Write your own newspaper. Find yourse[l]f a reporter's notebook and interview friends or members of your family abou[t] any interesting events that have happened. Write down what they say in[ ] your notebook, so you have it ready to use in your report. Remember to use **direct** and **reported speech** in your report.

Answers

1. *These are just examples of the sort of sentences you might make. You may have used different nouns.*

a) The <u>cat</u> sat on the <u>wall</u>.
or The <u>elephant</u> sat on the <u>hat</u>.
b) A <u>cow</u> jumped over the <u>moon</u>.
c) My <u>Dad</u> threw the <u>stick</u> into the <u>river</u>.
d) The <u>man</u> was waiting for a <u>bus</u>.
e) Asleep on the <u>grass</u> there was a great big <u>snake</u>.

2. *These are just examples – you may have chosen different names.*

a) <u>Cuddles</u> the cat   **d)** <u>Boris</u> the dog
b) <u>Florence</u> the fish   **e)** <u>Sid</u> the snake
c) <u>Ozzie</u> the hamster   **f)** <u>Arnie</u> the lizard

3. *Here are some examples of words you might have included on your three lists.*

Cake	Dog	Building
chocolate éclair	husky	supermarket
danish pastry	corgi	bank
jam roll	greyhound	school
bakewell tart	dalmatian	museum
jam donut	golden retriever	tower block
blueberry muffin	alsatian	factory

4. *These are just examples – you might have used different words to make the sentences more interesting.*

a) The <u>elephant</u> stole the <u>bananas</u>.
b) The <u>greyhound</u> ran into the <u>supermarket</u>.
c) The <u>princess</u> stood in the middle of the <u>ballroom</u>.
d) The <u>soldier</u> put on his <u>uniform</u>.
e) The <u>fire-fighters</u> came out of the <u>tower block</u>.

1. The <u>winding</u> path led her as far as the <u>crumbling</u> walls of an <u>abandoned</u> building. The walls were <u>overgrown with ivy</u> and the floor was <u>scattered with rough bricks and rubble.</u>

Answers

2. *These are just suggestions – there are many other adjectives that could be used.*

angry alligators
brown bears
cruel crocodiles
daft ducks
enchanting elephants
fearsome foxes
greedy gorillas
huge hippos
incredible insects
jolly jackals
kind kangaroos
lively lions
moody monkeys

noisy nightingales
odd otters
playful pandas
quarrelsome quails
rowdy rats
smooth snakes
terrifying tigers
ugly umbrella birds
vicious vultures
wild whales
young yaks
zany zebras

Page 7

3. *Here are some suggestions of adjectives you might have included. There are many others.*

Size	Colour	Qualities	Moods
enormous	golden	ugly	angry
huge	green	shy	happy
tiny	purple	kind	sad
minute	crimson	bad-tempered	miserable
short	lemon	beautiful	scared
slight	turquoise	friendly	cheerful

4. *This is just an example of adjectives that you might have used.*
The sky was <u>heavy</u> and <u>grey</u>. It was <u>cold</u> and a few <u>feathery</u> flakes of snow were beginning to fall. Suddenly out of the gloom a <u>hunched</u> figure appeared hurrying down the road. The figure was <u>bent</u> and <u>sinister-looking</u>. It was wearing a <u>dark flowing</u> cloak.

5. *These are just examples of adjectives that you might have used.*
a) ivy-covered walls
b) barred windows
c) heavy oak door
d) towering turrets
e) swirling flags

Page 8

1. a) clever ▶ cleverer ▶ cleverest
b) strong ▶ stronger ▶ strongest
c) fast ▶ faster ▶ fastest
d) cold ▶ colder ▶ coldest

Answers

2. *These are just suggestions of how you might have completed the sentences.*
a) My dad is <u>cleverer</u> than the winner of <u>Mastermind</u>.
b) Our dog is <u>noisier</u> than <u>six car alarms</u>.
c) My sister is <u>funnier</u> than <u>a Tom and Jerry cartoon</u>.
d) Our car is <u>faster</u> than a <u>speeding rocket</u>.

3. a) Wheat-a-Flakes – the <u>crunchiest</u> cereal yet.
b) Don't miss the <u>funniest</u> film of the year.
c) Test-drive the <u>fastest</u> car on the track.
d) This is the <u>creamiest</u> ice cream ever tasted.

Page 9

1. *You can insert in the boxes whatever numbers you like, but check the list below to make sure that you have got the plurals right.*

a) packets of crisps	**e)** bottles of pop
b) pizzas	**f)** bags of balloons
c) cakes	**g)** packs of streamers
d) cookies	

2. *These are just examples of some of the items you might see more than one of, depending on which room you are sitting in.*

books	children	people	chairs	cushions
windows	mugs	doors	shelves	tables

3. *These are just examples of plurals that you might have used.*
a) Onto his ark Noah took: two <u>monkeys</u>, two <u>elephants</u>, two <u>zebras</u> and lots of other animals.
b) At the market there were lots of things to buy: <u>books, toys, CDs</u> and many other things.

Page 10

1. a) We went to the shop but **it** was closed.
b) Mark had lost **his** coat and could not find **it** anywhere.
c) The twins were in the garden but **their** mum did not see **them**.
d) Nina knew that the book was **hers** but **she** did not want **it**.
e) The man was following **us** and **we** were worried.
f) Jordan thought **he** had won the race, but **he** should have looked behind **him**.

Page 11

2. The tortoise and the hare waited for the gun to start the race. Bang! Immediately **the hare** flew out of the blocks. His long legs ate up the ground and soon he was completely out of sight. Meanwhile **the tortoise** had only just crossed the starting line. His little legs did not move very fast. Looking back from the top of the hill **the hare** saw **the tortoise** and laughed.

3. a) It = the box
b) that = Eric going first
c) this = Nina winning
d) It = the disco

Answers

Page 12

1. a) The aeroplane <u>took off</u> and <u>soared</u> into the sky.
  b) From behind a tree, the cat <u>pounced</u> suddenly.
  c) Carly <u>listened</u> for a moment before she <u>stepped</u> forward and <u>spoke</u>.
  d) Tigers often <u>sleep</u> by day and <u>hunt</u> at night.

2. a) Mr Samuels **has** a frightening temper.
  b) Zebras **have** stripes.
  c) Paris **is** the capital city of France.
  d) Jamilla and Judith **are** twins.
  e) I **am** very happy today.

3. *There are other possible sentences that could be made.*
  a) The rain fell.   **c)** The king laughed.
  b) A building shook.   **d)** Marcie groaned.

Page 13

4. *These are just examples of powerful verbs that you could have used – there are lots of other possibilities.*
  a) The princess **glared** at the fisherman.
  b) The giant **stomped** across the hillside.
  c) The monster **gobbled** his food.
  d) The wind **howled** through the trees.
  e) 'It's not fair,' **moaned** Rashid.
  f) The man **clambered** into the car.

5. *This is just an example of powerful verbs that could be used in the description.*
  Grey-black clouds **rolled** across the sky. The branches on the trees **trembled** in the wind and the leaves **scattered** all around. Raindrops **splattered** on the windowpane and **exploded** in puddles on the pavement. People **scurried** down the road towards their homes. They **battled** with their umbrellas in the rain.

Page 14

1. slowly   loudly
    anxiously   smartly
    sweetly   carefully
    peacefully   madly
    quietly   cheerfully
    politely   excitedly

2. *These are just examples of adverbs that you could use – you may have chosen others.*
  a) Ten children singing <u>merrily</u>   **f)** Five children talking <u>excitedly</u>
  b) Nine children dancing <u>wildly</u>   **g)** Four children laughing <u>loudly</u>
  c) Eight children reading <u>quietly</u>   **h)** Three children watching <u>carefully</u>
  d) Seven children walking <u>slowly</u>   **i)** Two children running <u>madly</u>
  e) Six children waiting <u>anxiously</u>   **j)** And just one child sleeping <u>peacefully</u>

Answers

3. *These are not the only answers – the adverbs could be placed in different positions in the sentences.*
   a) The man spoke **angrily** to his neighbours.
   b) The princess moved across the room **gracefully**.
   c) He walked **carefully** along the plank.
   d) **Hurriedly**, he hid the letters under a book.

4. *These are just examples – you may have chosen other words.*
   a) The king **jumped** to his feet and **stormed** out of the chamber.
   b) The woman **glanced anxiously** around her as if she was **searching** for someone.
   c) Ed the elephant **greedily snatched** the buns and **crammed** them into his mouth.
   d) The boy **tore** down the road **screaming wildly**.

1. *These are just suggestions – other prepositional phrases could be used.*
   a) The boy climbed **over the fence**.
   b) The girl jumped **into the hole**.
   c) The man was standing **by the oak tree**.
   d) The car drove **through the city**.
   e) The ghost appeared **on the balcony**.
   f) Marcus fell **off his skateboard**.

2. *These are just suggestions – other prepositional phrases could be used.*
   a) Sally went for a run **before breakfast**.
   b) **At midnight** it began to rain.
   c) **During the night**, all was quiet.
   d) They couldn't go out **after tea**.
   e) **On Saturday** we went to the cinema.

3. *These are just suggestions – other prepositions would have the same effect.*
   a) The cat was sitting **in** the box.
   b) The path went **through** the wood.
   c) The boy scrambled **over** the hedge.
   d) Sophie walked **into** the river.
   e) George was hiding **behind** the dustbin.
   f) They arrived home **after** tea.

4. **a)** Mix the flour and sugar together **in** a large bowl.
   b) Heat the butter and milk **over** a low heat.
   c) Roll out the mixture **with** a rolling pin.
   d) Place the biscuits **on** a baking tray.
   e) Take the biscuits out of the oven **after** 20 minutes.
   f) Leave them to cool **before** tasting.

Answers

1. **a)** The children were hoping to go to the beach. **However**, it rained all day.
b) It was snowing heavily this morning. **As a result**, lots of people were late fo
school.
c) We visited the famous landmarks in Paris. **For example**, we went to the
Eiffel Tower.
d) Our train was over an hour late. **Eventually**, we arrived at our destination.
e) The trainers were not really what I wanted. **Also**, they were too expensive.
f) It was fine all day today. **In contrast**, it rained all yesterday.

2. *These are just examples of how the sentences might continue.*
a) Many people need to use their cars every day. **For example**, some people
drive to work.
b) Many people need to use their cars every day. **However**, some
people could use public transport instead.
c) Many people need to use their cars every day. **As a result**, there are too
many cars on the roads.
d) Many people need to use their cars every day. **After all**, cars provide the
easiest way of getting around.

3. *These are just suggestions. Other time connectives could be used.*
a) Red Riding Hood was walking through the forest.
b) Suddenly, a wolf jumped out and surprised her.
c) After that, Red Riding Hood went on her way again.
d) Meanwhile, the wolf rushed to Granny's house.
e) Later, Red Riding Hood arrived at Granny's house.
f) Now, the wolf tried to eat Red Riding Hood!
g) At that moment, a woodcutter rushed in and killed the wolf.
h) Finally, everyone was safe.

4. *These are just examples of how the sentences might continue.*
a) It has not rained for several weeks. **Consequently**, the ground is very dry.
b) The wind fills the sails of the yacht. **As a result**, the yacht moves forward.
c) The handles on the bag were not very strong. **Therefore**, they broke as soo
as something heavy was put in it.
d) The lions had not eaten for some time. **Because of this** they were very
dangerous.

5. *Some other conjunctions would also make sense in these sentences.*
a) The old man continued on his way **although** it was getting dark.
b) Do not enter the room **unless** a green light is showing.
c) Everyone rushed towards the river **as** the fire spread out of control.
d) He fell asleep in his chair **because** he was so tired.
e) When he saw the food, he gobbled it up immediately.

Answers

6. *There are many possible endings for these sentences – these are just suggestions.*
   a) The monster roared loudly **when** <u>he was annoyed.</u>
   b) The monster roared loudly **because** <u>someone had stepped on his tail.</u>
   c) The monster roared loudly **although** <u>there was no-one to hear him.</u>
   d) The monster roared loudly **until** <u>he realised no-one was listening.</u>
   e) The monster roared loudly **so** <u>we all ran away and hid.</u>
   f) The monster roared loudly **if** <u>he was not fed.</u>

Page 21 **I.** **a)** adjective   **d)** preposition
            b) noun   **e)** adverb
            c) verb   **f)** conjunction

2. *These are just examples of the kinds of sentences you could write.*
   a) The chattering monkey swings through the trees.
   b) An extra supply came just in time.
   c) The magic carpet flew away.
   d) A cool computer game is now available.
   e) The best player scored before half time.
   f) A new boy arrived in the afternoon.

Page 22 **I.** *Here is one example of how you could make this description more impressive – but you will probably have chosen different words.*

A pair of giant   were flung open   stunning
~~Two big~~ gold doors ~~opened~~/to show the ~~lovely~~ ballroom. The room
as long as a tennis court   crammed   elegantly dressed
was/~~very long~~ and/full of/people, all dancing. The walls were ~~all~~
     as snow   with a mosaic   ruby -
white/and the ceiling was patterned/. There were/~~lovely~~ red curtains
          tall   gleaming   polished In the far distance
hanging at the/windows. The/floor was made of/stone. ~~Right~~/at the
                   enormous golden thrones ,majestic,   silver stage
end of the ballroom, were two/~~big, gold~~ chairs standing/on a/~~platform.~~

2. *Here is one example of how you could make this story more exciting – but you will probably have chosen different words.*
        rushed   grabbed   grey stone   emerald-green
Casper/~~ran~~ forward and ~~took~~/the burning torch from the/wall. The/dragon
  spun   glared   Terrified,   furious
~~turned~~/round and/~~looked~~ at him./Casper waved the torch at the/dragon. The
    slowly   suddenly Black s   billowed
dragon/put his head back and/roared. /~~Smoke~~ ~~came~~/out of his nose and
          shot from   cavernous   blast of fiery   retreat hastily
flames/~~came out of~~ his/mouth. The ~~hot~~/breath made Casper/~~go back~~.

Page 23

3. *These are just suggestions, other verbs could be used.*
Prince Fortune <u>strode</u> into the hall. He <u>glanced</u> across the room to where the Queen and Princess were <u>whispering</u> together.

4. *This is just one possibility – you may have selected different adjectives.*
Three butterflies danced together in the ~~bright, dazzling, glorious~~ early morning sunshine. They fluttered their ~~vivid, bright, vibrant,~~ colourful wings as they danc their ~~merry,~~ graceful, ~~clever~~ dance of friendship. The three butterflies were always happy~~, cheerful and merry~~ to be together. But just then a ~~big, horrible,~~ threatening~~, dark~~ rain cloud passed in front of the bright, ~~dazzling, glorious~~ sun.

5. a) Too much sugar can <u>cause</u> teeth to <u>decay</u>.
   b) A telescope is an <u>instrument</u> that makes <u>distant</u> objects seem nearer.
   c) The Moon <u>orbits</u> the Earth.

Page 24

1. *These are just possibilities – you may have chosen a different version of the sentences.*
   a) The Princess **carelessly** threw the bottle **out of the window**.
   b) At midnight, the villagers were waiting **anxiously**.
   c) Frequently, the explorers went without any food **during this time**.
   d) He was **usually** in trouble **at school**.

2. *Your sentences can be in any order but should include the following three versions.*
   a) He strode purposefully through the town.
   b) Purposefully, he strode through the town.
   c) Through the town he strode purposefully.

Page 26

1. a) It **was** hot last week.
   b) I **heard** a strange sound.
   c) I **jumped** high.
   d) I **took** my time.
   e) Ed **ran** for the bus.

2. a) It **will be** hot tomorrow
   b) Jill **will be** late tomorrow.
   c) I **will help** to wash-up.
   d) We **shall have** our breakfast at eight o'clock. *or* We **will have** our breakfa at eight o'clock.

3. *The answers given are just examples – but check that you have used the correct tense.*
   a) Earlier the three bears **went** out for a walk.
   b) At the moment Goldilocks **is** asleep in the three bears' cottage.
   c) Later, the bears **will return** home.

Answers

ge 27   **4.** Johnston **crossed** from the left. A shot **came** in from Liddell. It **bounced** off a defender. Liddell **fired** the ball back towards goal, but the goalkeeper **saved** easily.

5. *This is just an example. Make sure you have used the future tense.*
There <u>will be</u> many exciting opportunities. Making the right choice <u>will bring</u> you wealth and good fortune.

ge 28   **1. a)** first person
  b) third person
  c) third person
  d) second person
  e) first person

2. Lucy is 11 years old and she goes to Midfield School in Stonington.
When she grows up she would like to be a singer and have a hit CD.

ge 29   **3.** I had been working all day, but still I had not caught one fish. I pulled up the last of my nets – it was empty, like all the others. I thought how unlucky I was. What would I tell my children? Just then, something in the water caught my eye. I looked over the side of the boat to get a better look...

ge 30   **1. a)** I plays for the school team. ✗
  b) We were really pleased.✓
  c) I has some money to spend. ✗
  d) They am waiting for the bus. ✗
  e) You have five more minutes.✓
  f) I hates cheese and onion crisps. ✗

2. *These are the corrected sentences. It doesn't matter if you have written them in a different order.*
  a) I <u>play</u> for the school team.
  c) I <u>have</u> some money to spend.
  d) They <u>are</u> waiting for the bus.
  f) I <u>hate</u> cheese and onion crisps.

3. a) You <u>are</u> happy.
  b) She <u>has</u> lots of friends.
  c) I <u>am</u> pleased.
  d) They <u>have</u> a beautiful house.
  e) He <u>is</u> tired.

ge 31   **1.**
                                                          to
On Saturday we went/watch the school football team play in the
                    was   *which*
Player's Cup. It/a very exciting game. The final score was 2–2,/was

probably a fair result because both teams played well. Our team scored
                              a
first, thanks to/magnificent free kick from Lee Edwards. But then they
                                          for
equalised just before the whistle went/half time.

Answers

2. Let me tell you about my family. We ~~lives~~/*live* in a house on the corner of Grant Street. I ~~has~~/*have* two sisters and a brother. My sisters ~~is~~/*are* twins. My brother i older than me. Sometimes we all ~~plays~~/*play* together, but sometimes we argue.

Page 32

1. *These are just suggestions – there are many ways to complete the sentences.*
   a) The angry lion <u>glared</u> through the bars of the cage.
   b) The valuable vase <u>shattered</u> into pieces on the floor.
   c) The rabbit <u>had</u> two pointed ears.
   d) It <u>rained</u> on the way to school.
   e) The excited children <u>screeched</u> loudly.

2. *See the words that are underlined above. All of them are verbs.*

3. *You may have ended your sentences differently.*
   a) The horse **trotted** down the road.
   b) The rock climbers **clambered** to the top of the cliff.
   c) The wizard **vanished** in a puff of smoke.
   d) A butterfly **fluttered** past the window.
   e) A dog **barked** outside.

Page 33

4. a) The man drove the sports car.
   b) The boy ate his breakfast.
   c) The child screamed out of the window.
   d) The inventor made a robot.
   e) Tarik watched the television.

5. a) Charles Dickens was born in 1812.
   b) James Watt was an inventor.
   c) Gorillas are the largest of the apes.
   d) Polar bears live in the Arctic.
   e) Today it is sunny.

Page 34

1. *You may have chosen different phrases to complete the sentences.*
   a) In the morning, the teacher was furious with the class.
   b) Just a moment later the robber escaped in a car.
   c) Only the other day a boy slipped over in the corridor.

2. a) Paula, who was exhausted, refused to move.
   b) Mr King, who had left early, was now very late.
   c) The beggar, who was blind, pleaded for help.

58 Grammar

Schofield & Sims | Understanding En

Answers

1. **a)** I missed the bus **but** I wasn't late.

b) The windows were open **so** everyone could hear him singing.

c) He picked up all the rubbish **and** he put it in the bin.

d) It will be dry in the north **but** there will be rain in the south.

e) We could go to the zoo **or** we could go into town.

2. *These are just suggestions, the sentences could be finished in many ways.*

a) The car stopped **and** <u>two policemen jumped out.</u>

b) The car stopped **but** <u>no-one got out.</u>

c) Jack was bored **so** <u>he switched on the television.</u>

d) Jack was bored **and** <u>fed up.</u>

e) Simone loved to play football **but** <u>she was not chosen for the team.</u>

f) Simone loved to play football **so** <u>she played every day.</u>

1. *These are only suggestions. You might have made different sentences.*

a) As it was dark, I went straight to bed.

b) When we arrived home, I went straight to bed.

c) I ran away because I was feeling miserable.

d) I ran away when it was dark.

e) It was dark when we arrived home.

2. **a)** Standing by the door, Ellen watched the storm approaching.

b) Waving his arms madly, the man shouted for help.

c) Travelling fast, the car just missed the approaching lorry.

3. *These are just suggestions – there are other ways of combining the sentences.*

a) As the sun began to rise, making the grey world lighter, the birds awoke from their sleep.

b) Feeling confident, Lee climbed straight to the top of the ladder without looking down.

c) The long-haired sloth is a slow-moving mammal that lives in trees.

d) Walking quickly, he followed the mysterious figure through the marketplace.

e) The rocks are worn away and become smooth as the waves wash over them.

1. _____ main clause .... subordinate clause

a) The dog snarled at her, growling menacingly.

b) With his heart pounding, Dean stepped forward.

c) While she was reading, the doorbell rang.

d) The lights came on one at a time until the whole street was lit up.

e) When the factory closed, many people lost their jobs.

f) Stretch the fabric over the card, folding the edges under neatly.

Answers

2. a) <u>Until the storm began,</u> everything was quiet.
   b) <u>Humming merrily,</u> the man strolled along the street.
   c) <u>Despite playing extra time,</u> the match was still a draw.

Page 39 **1.** *This is just one way of combining the sentences – you may have found a different way.*

One day Phil and Leon went to the canal. ~~They were~~ /going ^{to go} fishing. There

seemed to be no-one else around. ^{so t}/They chose the best place. ~~They~~ ^{and} started to

get out the rods./ ^{Suddenly,} ~~Then~~ there was a loud splash/ ^{followed by} ~~Then there was~~ a scream. /Ph

and Leon looked up. ^{, t}/They saw something moving in the water. <u>Then ~~they saw~~</u> ^{There was}

a hand waving. Someone had fallen into the water.

2. *This is just one way of splitting up the single sentence into several – you may have found a different way.*

Like all animals, human beings need food in order to live.

~~because~~ /every ^E part of the body needs a steady supply of food so

that it can work properly, ~~but~~ /first ^{. F} the food has to be broken

down through a process called digestion/ ~~so that it can~~ dissolve in ^{. This allows the food to}

the blood and travel around the body.

Page 40 **1. a)** Statement: You are planning a holiday.
      Question: Are you planning a holiday?
   b) Statement: It is cold.
      Question: Is it cold?
   c) Statement: You are bored.
      Question: Are you bored?
   d) Statement: You can help me.
      Question: Can you help me?

2. a) Take the dog for a walk every day.
   b) Go to visit Hammington Hall this weekend.
   c) Eat lots of fruit and vegetables.
   d) Stack the chairs neatly.

Answers

3. a) Help me.
   b) Hold this end.
   c) Try this.
   d) Try this new ice cream.
   e) Come and visit soon.

4. a) Question
   b) Command
   c) Statement

5. *Here is one example of the kind of advert you may have written.*
   Question: Bored by slow computer games that are much too easy and dull?
   Statement: Manic Heroes is a new computer game for kids – it's wild, it's fast...
   Command: Try it now!

1.

	Positive	Negative
a)	Drop litter on the floor.	*Do not drop litter on the floor.*
b)	Everybody can help.	*Nobody can help.*
c)	*We can save the planet.*	We cannot save the planet.
d)	Everything is finished.	*Nothing is finished.*
e)	We always go swimming on Mondays.	*We never go swimming on Mondays.*

2. *These are just examples of the sort of sentences you should have written.*
   a) I can swim, but I **never** swim in the sea.
   b) I can see your problem, but I can**not** help you.
   c) I did kick the ball, but I **did not** break the window.
   d) Lots of people were there, but **nobody** saw me.

3. a) I never said anything.
   b) Nobody did anything to help.
   c) I saw nobody. (*or* I saw no-one.)
   d) I don't like anything here. (*or* I like nothing here.)

1. *These are just suggestions of the sort of endings needed.*
   a) If it is sunny at the weekend, I will play outside.
   b) If I were famous, I would live in a huge mansion.
   c) If I won the lottery, I would take a very long holiday.
   d) If I worked hard, I would do well at school.
   e) If I had a magic carpet, I would fly round the world.
   f) If I ruled the world, I would stop all wars.

2. *These are only suggestions of the sort of endings needed.*
  a) If we continue to destroy forests, soon there will be none left.
  b) If everyone drops litter in the street, then the town will become dirty.
  c) If everyone switched off one light, we would save a lot of energy.
  d) If Jack decides to climb the beanstalk, he might be in danger.
  e) If they cannot escape from the dragon's cave, they will be eaten.

Page 44

You can choose whatever name you like, but make sure you have written the word correctly as direct speech.
  1. a) 'What's the matter?' asked Squirrel.
      'I've lost my way,' moaned Mouse.
  b) 'What shall we do now?' asked Jack.
      'Run for it!' shouted Jill.
  c) 'I think we're nearly there,' said Jill.
      'I hope you are right,' puffed Jack.
  d) 'You shall go to the ball!' announced the Fairy Godmother.
      'But how?' asked Cinderella.

Page 45 **2. a)** Suddenly Judith shouted that she knew the answer.
  b) Michael asked whether they could follow their footsteps back through the forest.
  c) George explained that the dog must have buried the key in the garden.
  d) Rebecca said that it was all her fault.

3. a) Mr Paul said he could not believe what was happening.
  b) Miss Jackson asked whether they would get their money back.
  c) Mr Patel said that his family were (*or* had been) very worried.
  d) Dr Archer said that she will (*or* would) certainly be writing a letter of complain

Page 46 **1. a)** A play was put on by the children.
  b) The show was enjoyed by everybody.
  c) The factory was destroyed by a fire.
  d) The crowd was silenced by a whistle.
  e) Fatima was surprised by the sudden noise.

2. *These are just suggestions – you probably ended your sentences differently.*
  a) The plate was broken by my baby sister Bimla.
  b) The bag of gold was stolen by the wicked elves.
  c) The man was hurt by the suggestion that he had lied.
  d) The car was damaged by the falling tree.
  e) The lion was captured by the brave zoo-keeper.

age 47 **3. a)** Pigeons were used to send messages.
   b) The headteacher was annoyed.
   c) A letter was sent to the Prime Minister.
   d) The pirates' treasure was stolen.
   e) People were asked for their opinions.

   4. a) The plants were watered every day.
   b) The Mayor was invited to the show.
   c) The wires were attached to the battery.
   d) Salt was added to the water.
   e) A lot of ideas were discussed.

Grammar checklist for writing

Writing fiction (stories)

When you are writing stories, remember the following points.

- Use adjectives and precise nouns to make descriptions interesting.

- Use powerful verbs to describe feelings and actions.

- Include some direct and some reported speech.

- Don't slip from the first to the third person.

- Don't slip from the past tense to the present tense.

- Use time connectives to tell your reader when events happened.

- Take care with pronouns – is it clear who 'he' or 'she' is?

- A few short sentences can be good for impact – but not too many!

- Complex sentences are better than lots of simple sentences.

Writing non-fiction (fact)

When you are writing non-fiction, remember the following points.

- Use precise and accurate nouns.

- Only use adjectives and adverbs when they are really needed.

- Use connectives to link together your ideas.

- Use the right tense (recounts are written in the past tense, but reports are written in the present tense).

- Do not keep referring to the name of the subject you are writing about – use pronouns for variety.

- Use complex sentences to help make links between ideas.

- Use passive sentences to make your writing sound more formal.